EGMONT
We bring stories to life

First published in Great Britain 2010
by Egmont UK Limited,
239 Kensington High Street, London W8 6SA

Group Art Editor: Jeanette Ryall • Group Editor: Keilly Swift
• Designer: Anni Nolan • Writer: Olivia McLearon

© 2010 Disney Enterprises, Inc.

ISBN 978 1 4052 5471 7
1 3 5 7 9 10 8 6 4 2
Printed in Italy

playhouse
Disney

SM

This Annual
belongs
to

Name......................................

Age...

playhouse Disney

ANNUAL 2011

All of this inside ...

MICKEY MOUSE! CLUBHOUSE

Seeing Sheep	12
Cloud Pictures	14
Pluto's Kennel	15
Phone a Friend	18
Story: Hurdle Hounds	26
Roller Race	28
Top Trophy	29
Falling Objects	38
Lift Off	39
Home Search	46
Mickey's Lullaby	56
Golden Harp	57
Picnic Party	64

little einsteins

Pretty Petra	20
Flying High	30
Speedy Colours	31
Big and Small Machine	34
Space Explorer	36
Shaping Up	37
Create an Orchestra	54
How Old are You?	68

HANDY MANNY

Story: Rabbits on the Run	08
Pretty Parrots	10
Bouncing Balls	11
Green-Fingered Friends	16
Seeing Double	24
Snow Sledge	25
Fun with Sound	32
Story: Far from Home	42
Painting Page	45
Manny's Band	50
Karaoke Fun	52
Radio Tunes	53
Happy Birthday, Manny	60
A Gift for Manny	62
Manny's Cake	63

JUNGLE JUNCTION

Finding Friends	22
Speeding Home	48
Crocker's Party	66

SPECIAL AGENT OSO

Oso's Mission	40
Rope Tangle	41
Special Song	58

Rabbits Or

All about
ANIMALS

1

One day, Manny and his Tools
went to their local pet store.
The owner greeted them, cheerfully,
showing them the rabbit cage door.

2

The lock on the cage was broken,
and it needed to be repaired.
"I can fix that," thought Manny,
he was always well prepared.

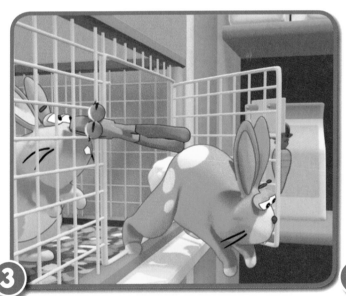

3

Squeeze, the pliers, was on the case,
and she started without delay.
But while the cage door was open,
the RABBITS all hopped away.

The RABBITS
are hopping!

4

However hard Manny tried,
he couldn't catch each bunny.
The hopping RABBITS were far too fast,
and they thought it was very funny!

Can you SPOT these objects
within the story?

The Run

5 Just then, Manny had a good idea,
remembering what RABBITS eat.
He spotted some carrots, on a shelf,
they'd be the perfect rabbit treat!

6 Manny quickly fetched the carrots,
and made a yummy trail.
Soon, the RABBITS started to munch,
he knew it wouldn't fail!

7 The RABBITS moved across the store,
as Manny watched, with a grin.
The final carrot was at the cage,
and the RABBITS hopped straight in!

8 Quickly, Squeeze finished her repair,
and locked the RABBITS inside.
"Good work, Tools. That job's done!"
a happy Manny cried!

Bouncing Balls

Handy Manny is playing ball with his pet Fix-It. Help them **COLOUR** each row of balls to match the top one.

Show your children that traffic lights have a colour sequence, too!

Woof, woof!

FiX-iT

11

Seeing Sheep

Daisy is counting sheep. Join in with her and **COUNT** the number of sheep in each group. **WRITE** the numbers in the circles.

Can you see a sheep-shaped bus

Will you help me count?

1

Baaa!

Try making funny farm animal noises with your children!

1 — **2** — **3**

Cloud Pictures

Donald is drawing three pictures he can see in the clouds. Can you MATCH the cloud pictures to the animals?

Pluto's Kennel

? Can you **FIND** the **3** shapes at the bottom of the page in Pluto's kennel? **COLOUR** each one as you spot it!

PLUTO

? What shapes can your children spot in the objects around your home?

Triangle   **Square**   **Circle**

Green-Fingered Friends

Manny, Kelly and the Tools are helping Abuelito with his garden. Can you can TRACE the trails to help Abuelito, too?

16

Help your children to learn their home phone number. Ask them to repeat it every day until they know it by heart!

Pretty Petra

WOW! We've crossed the ocean and now we're in JORDAN, in a city that was carved into the ROCK. In fact, its name is the Greek word for rock: PETRA!

Let's discover together!

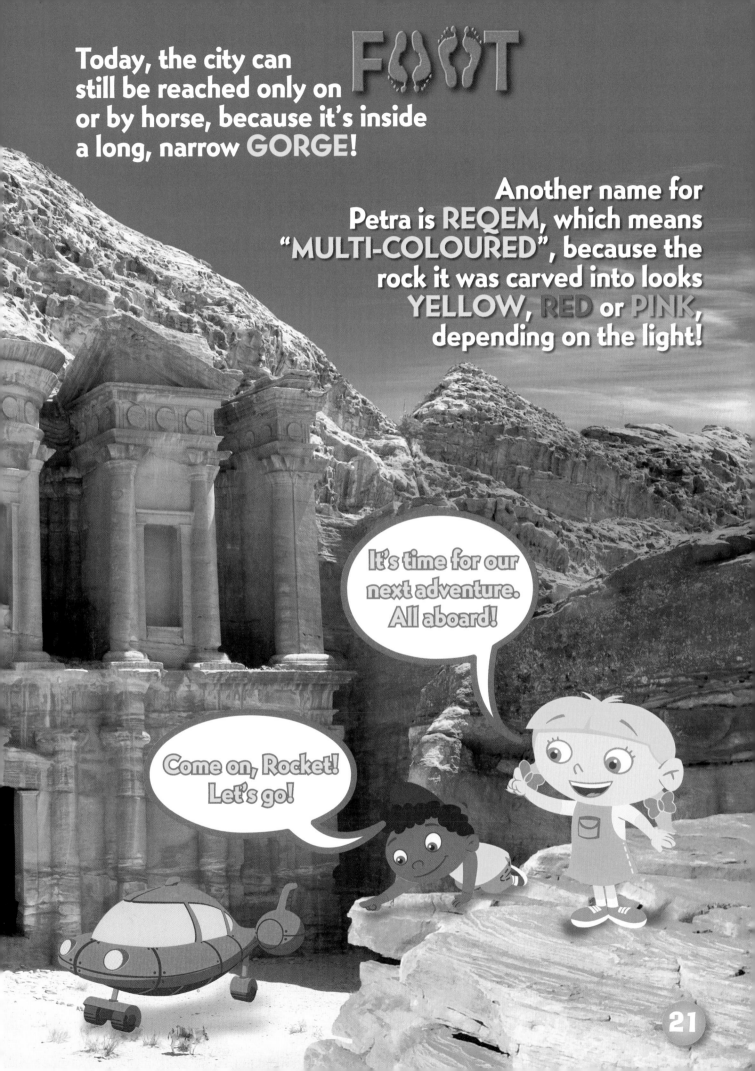

Finding Friends

? TRACE over the letters. Can you SAY the names out loud?

Hippobus

Bungo

? Can you FIND the Jungle Junction friends in the picture? TICK the box when you find each one.

Ellyvan

Zooter

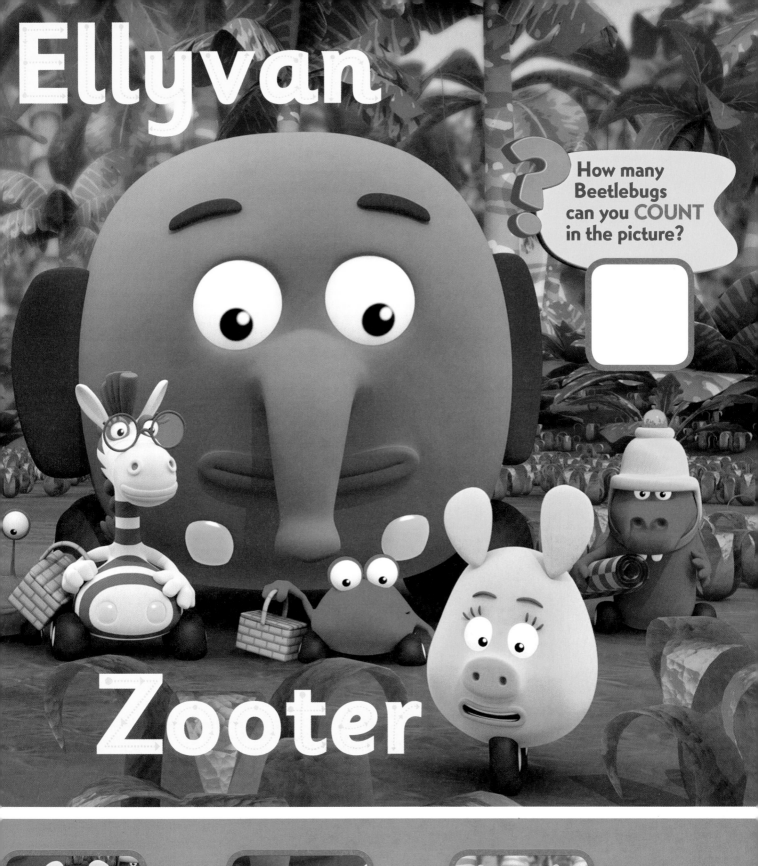

How many Beetlebugs can you COUNT in the picture?

23

Seeing Double

Manny has found 5 differences in the bottom picture. Can you FIND them all? COLOUR a bolt each time you find one.

Answers: The top of the trophy is yellow, the plaque is missing from the front of the trophy, Stretch is missing, Dusty's eyes are looking the other way and the knob on the drawer is missing.

24

Snow Sledge

Can you **WORK OUT** how Manny built his snow sledge? **CIRCLE** the 3 pieces he chose.

1

One morning, Goofy announced,
There was to be a hurdle race.
"It's just for dogs," he giggled,
"With a **TROPHY** for first place!"

2

So, Pluto and Butch, the bulldog,
Stood side-by-side, in a row,
And waited for the race to start.
Goofy called, "Ready, steady, go!"

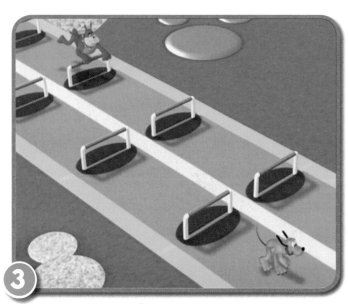

3

But Butch was big and heavy,
Which made him very slow.
And Pluto soon raced ahead,
He put on quite a show!

4

Suddenly, Pluto ran extra fast.
Something had caught his eye!
He ran off the hurdle track,
Chasing a pretty butterfly!

Can you SPOT these details in the story?

Hounds

5

Mickey Mouse grabbed his whistle,
And then he blew on it, hard.
"Pluto, get back on track!"
Mickey called, across the yard.

6

When Pluto heard the whistle,
He stopped and did a spin.
But would he reach the track,
In time to beat Butch and win?

7

As Pluto jumped the final hurdle,
Mickey shouted, "You'll be fine!"
And then, ahead of Butch,
Pluto crossed the finish line!

8

The shiny TROPHY made them proud,
Winning the race had been tricky.
"Pluto, you flew over those hurdles,
Like a butterfly!" laughed Mickey.

Roller Race

Who won the roller race? **FOLLOW** the paths to find out!

This is fun!

Can your children name something else they play with that has wheels?

1

2

3

28

Answer: Goofy won the race!

Top Trophy

Which SHAPES can you see on the trophy? Now add some COLOUR!

Shape up!

Star **Circle**

Triangle **Square**

29

Speedy Colours

Add some **COLOUR**, as quick as you can, to help Annie celebrate her win!

Fun with Sound

MAKE a paper cup telephone! **ASK** an adult to cut a tiny hole in the bottom of two paper cups. **THREAD** some string through the holes and **KNOT** each end. **GIVE** one cup to a friend, **PULL** the string tight and have a conversation!

Hello, Tools!

Hello!

Now ROLL a piece of card into a cone. SPEAK into the cone to MAGNIFY the sound!

Big and Small Machine

Uh-oh, the Little Einsteins have shrunk to a tiny size! Can you LEAD them to the Big and Small Machine, to return them to normal size again? WATCH OUT for the giant insects!

Space Explorer

Leo has landed on the moon! JOIN the dots in number order to complete the picture, then ADD some bright space colours!

Can your children point to the moon and pretend to hold it between their thumb and index finger?

1

2

3

10

9

6

4

8

7 5

36

Shaping Up

? The Little Einsteins are finding out about shapes! What SHAPE are these buildings?

Egypt

Mexico

France

Kukulcan

Saqqara

Louvre

Answer: the buildings are pyramid shape.

Falling Objects

Mickey has been bumped on the head by a falling apple! Can you **CIRCLE** the odd one out in each row of objects? Now **POINT** to the row with the heaviest objects.

With your children, throw a feather up into the air and count how many seconds it takes to reach the ground.

38

Lift Off

Mickey needs your help to launch his rocket. **TRACE** over the numbers from 5 down to 1 and **SAY** them out loud to **COMPLETE** the countdown!

Can you **FIND** Goofy?

Good job!

5

4

3

2

1

LIFT OFF!

Oso's Mission

Mr. Dos has given Special Agent Oso a new mission. Help him reach his destination by finding the 5 DIFFERENCES in the bottom picture.

Count them as you go!

Answer: Special Agent Dotty's eyes are blue, her microphone has disappeared, the buttons on her front have disappeared, Special Agent Oso's ear is missing and his nose is green.

40

Rope Tangle

Special Agent Oso needs to get down! Can you **HELP** him choose the right rope?

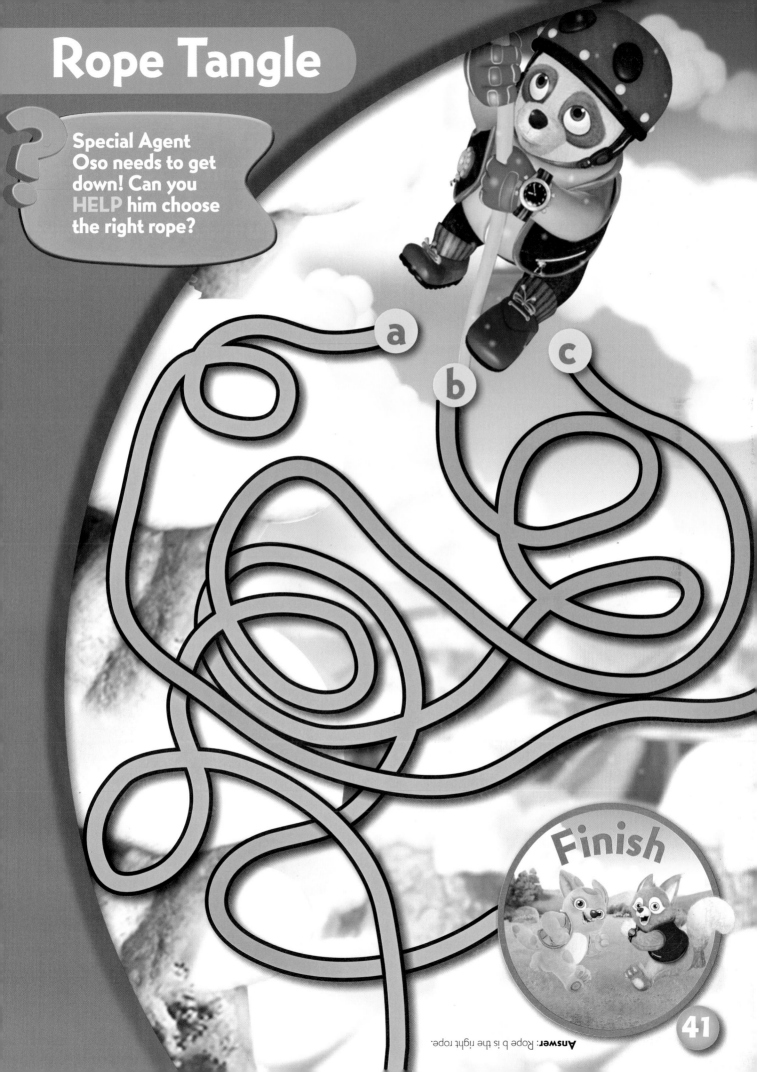

a

b

c

Finish

Answer: Rope b is the right rope.

All about HOMES

Far from

When Pat goes missing,

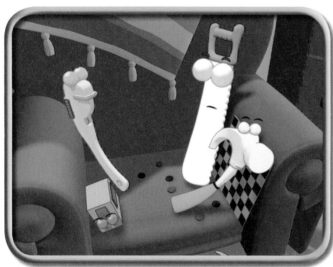

When he'd finished and was driving back to his shop, Manny noticed that Mrs. Portillo was having a garage sale. He stopped the car and he and the Tools all went out to take a look.

One morning, Handy Manny had a tough job to do. It was waking up his sleepy tools! **Pat, the hammer,** was particularly tired. He even slept in the car when Manny set off to fix a customer's **washing machine.**

"Ah, Manny! Is there anything you fancy buying?" Mrs. Portillo asked. "I'll take a look!" replied Manny. "And while you're here, please will you take a look at my toaster? It's stopped working," she added. "Sure, no problem," Manny said, and he headed into the house to get started.

42

Home

how will he get **home**?

Pat was still struggling to stay awake. So, he sneaked away from the other tools and into a **red box** on the table to take a nap.

But Pat didn't realise that the **red box** was for sale! Soon, Mrs. Portillo had sold it to a man and he carried it home with sleeping Pat still inside.

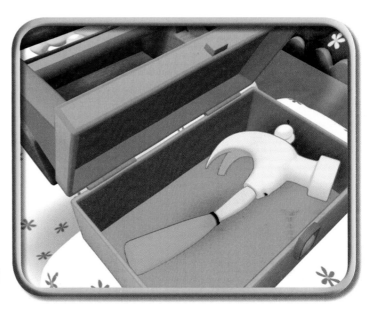

Before long, Manny and the Tools noticed that Pat was missing. "Where can he be?" Manny wondered.

Just then, Mrs. Portillo remembered the **red box** and had an idea about where Pat was.
"Oh no! I hope you can find him, Manny!" she cried.
"Don't worry, Mrs. Portillo, we'll get him back," Manny said, setting off.

He and the Tools began to search the town, looking for the man who had bought the **red box**.
"There he is!" **Stretch** cried, pointing to a man crossing the road, carrying a **red box**.

But when Manny caught up with the man, it was the wrong man and the wrong **red box**!

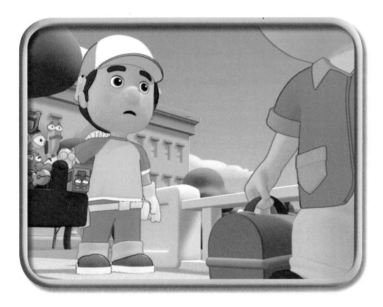

Meanwhile, the man who had bought the **red box** from Mrs. Portillo had arrived home. "I can't wait to put my stuff in this box!" he thought, as he opened it up. He was very surprised to find Pat inside!

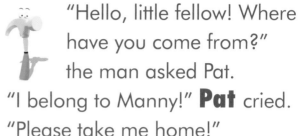

"Hello, little fellow! Where have you come from?" the man asked Pat. "I belong to Manny!" **Pat** cried. "Please take me home!"

By the time Manny and his tools arrived back at his shop, the man and Pat were there, waiting for them. "I found him sleeping in my new **red box**," the man explained. "Thank you for bringing him back to me!" Manny laughed. "It wasn't nice being so far from home. I'm so happy to be back!" Pat told the other tools.

The End

Home Search

Let's count!

1 2 3 4 5

Can your children count the number of windows and doors in your home?

1 2 3 4 5

Can you TRACE over the numbers?

47

Speeding Home

Zooter and Ellyvan need to reach Jungle Junction. Can you help them **FIND** their way to the middle?

Start

JUNGLE JUNCTION

Finish

Which friends can you **SEE** in the middle?

The Beetlebugs need to get home. **TRACE** over their trails to help them speed along!

Home

Home

Home

Manny's Band

Manny and the Tools are making music together. Can you **FIND** all the instruments in the scene? **TICK** the boxes as you spot them.

Xylophone

Drum

Trumpet

Guitar

Maracas

Tambourine

Castanets

Karaoke Fun

? Manny is taking part in a karaoke competition. Can you add some COLOUR to the picture? Sing a song while you colour him in!

Why not sing a duet with your child if they don't want to sing on their own?

Radio Tunes

Manny has fixed the radio. DRAW LINES to link the matching notes. Now CIRCLE the note left over and COLOUR the note in the box to match.

53

Create an Orchestra

FIND or MAKE a musical instrument for each of your friends to play. TAKE TURNS to be the conductor. Can you all START and STOP playing at the same time?

Can you MATCH these sounds to the instruments?

BANG!
CLAK!
SHAKE!
TOOT!

Encore!

We love music!

Bravo!

Ask your children to gently tap on different objects in the home with a kitchen utensil. How many new sounds can they discover?

Golden Harp

TRACE over the dotted lines to draw the strings on Mickey's golden harp. Can you POINT to the shortest string?

Special Song

Can you **FOLLOW** the three special steps to complete a mission, just like Agent Oso?

Step 1

Sing the song to the tune of 'Round and Round the Garden'.

You're on a special mission like Agent Oso bear! One step, two step, three step and you're there!

Step 2
Write your Special Agent name.

Special Agent ---------------------------------

Step 3
Colour in your special medal. You've completed your assignment. Well done!

Happy Birth

1

On the morning of Manny's birthday,
The Tools decorated the shop.
"One last streamer," Dusty cried out,
"Before it's time to stop!"

2

The gang had only just finished,
When Manny came through the door.
"Wow!" he cried. "What a surprise!
I couldn't have wished for more!"

3

"Happy birthday!" sang the Tools,
As loudly as they could.
"Now, let's get the party started!"
They knew it was going to be good!

4

The Tools led Manny to the piñata,
A hanging star filled with sweets.
He put on a blindfold and used a stick,
To break it to reach the treats!

Can you **SPOT** these details in the story?

5 Manny's first swing hit the piñata,
And the sweets came tumbling out.
"Hooray!" cried Manny, with a grin,
He had given it quite a clout!

6 "That one's mine!" Rusty cried,
Grabbing a sweet with one bite.
The Tools were very excited,
They'd never seen such a sight!

7 At that moment, a voice called out,
"Where's the birthday boy?"
Kind-hearted Kelly had baked a cake,
And she carried it in, full of joy.

8 "Thank you, Kelly!" said Manny, happily,
"I'm pleased you could be here."
He blew out the candle, making a wish,
To have fun, every day of the year!

A Gift for Manny

Felipe

Turner

Can you **HELP** Turner And Felipe **FIND 5** differences in the bottom picture? Colour a picture of Dusty as you spot each one.

Manny's Cake

Manny can't wait to taste the cake Kelly baked for him! Can you COLOUR the picture?

63

Picnic Party

Mickey and his friends are having a picnic party! Can you **DRAW** some more tasty food on to the picnic rug?

Can you **FIND** Pluto?

How many of each object can you **COUNT** in the scene? Write the numbers in the boxes. Then **TRACE** over the numbers?

1 2 3 4 5

6 7 8 9 10

Answers: There are 5 glasses of juice, 2 hot dogs, 3 presents, 1 bowl of sweets and 7 balloons.

? COLOUR IN each balloon the same colour as the Beetlebug holding it.

How Old Are You?

? The Little Einsteins are all saying their ages. Can you WRITE over the numbers? Now FILL IN the card below.

I am

I am

I am

I am

I am

_ _ _ _ _ _ _ _ _ _ _ _ _ _

years old

My birthday is

_ _ _ _ _ _ _ _ _ _ _ _ _ _